2018

JANUARY

M	T	W	T	F	S	S
1	2	3	4	5	6	7
8	9	10	11	12	13	14
15	16	17	18	19	20	21
22	23	24	25	26	27	28
29	30	31				

FEBRUARY

M	T	W	T	F	S	S
			1	2	3	4
5	6	7	8	9	10	11
12	13	14	15	16	17	18
19	20	21	22	23	24	25
26	27	28				

MARCH

M	T	W	T	F	S	S
			1	2	3	4
5	6	7	8	9	10	11
12	13	14	15	16	17	18
19	20	21	22	23	24	25
26	27	28	29	30	31	

APRIL

M	T	W	T	F	S	S
						1
2	3	4	5	6	7	8
9	10	11	12	13	14	15
16	17	18	19	20	21	22
23	24	25	26	27	28	29
30						

MAY

M	T	W	T	F	S	S
	1	2	3	4	5	6
7	8	9	10	11	12	13
14	15	16	17	18	19	20
21	22	23	24	25	26	27
28	29	30	31			

JUNE

M	T	W	T	F	S	S
				1	2	3
4	5	6	7	8	9	10
11	12	13	14	15	16	17
18	19	20	21	22	23	24
25	26	27	28	29	30	

JULY

M	T	W	T	F	S	S
						1
2	3	4	5	6	7	8
9	10	11	12	13	14	15
16	17	18	19	20	21	22
23	24	25	26	27	28	29
30	31					

AUGUST

M	T	W	T	F	S	S
		1	2	3	4	5
6	7	8	9	10	11	12
13	14	15	16	17	18	19
20	21	22	23	24	25	26
27	28	29	30	31		

SEPTEMBER

M	T	W	T	F	S	S
					1	2
3	4	5	6	7	8	9
10	11	12	13	14	15	16
17	18	19	20	21	22	23
24	25	26	27	28	29	30

OCTOBER

M	T	W	T	F	S	S
1	2	3	4	5	6	7
8	9	10	11	12	13	14
15	16	17	18	19	20	21
22	23	24	25	26	27	28
29	30	31				

NOVEMBER

M	T	W	T	F	S	S
			1	2	3	4
5	6	7	8	9	10	11
12	13	14	15	16	17	18
19	20	21	22	23	24	25
26	27	28	29	30		

DECEMBER

M	T	W	T	F	S	S
					1	2
3	4	5	6	7	8	9
10	11	12	13	14	15	16
17	18	19	20	21	22	23
24	25	26	27	28	29	30
31						

PERSONAL INFORMATION

NAME:
....

ADDRESS:
....
....

HOME TEL:
....

MOBILE:
....

EMAIL:
....

IN CASE OF EMERGENCY PLEASE CONTACT:
....

NAME:
....

ADDRESS:
....
....

HOME TEL:
....

MOBILE:
....

EMAIL:
....

DOCTOR:
....

BLOOD GROUP:
....

ALLERGIES:
....

NATIONAL INSURANCE Nº:
....

CAR REGISTRATION Nº:
....

PASSPORT Nº:

CONVERSIONS

WEIGHT

METRIC	IMPERIAL
50g	2oz
75g	2½oz
100g	4oz
125g	4½oz
150g	5oz
175g	6oz
200g	7oz
225g	8oz
250g	9oz
300g	11oz
350g	12oz
400g	14oz
450g	1lb
500g	1lb 2oz
550g	1lb 4oz
600g	1lb 5oz
650g	1lb 7oz
700g	1lb 9oz
750g	1lb 10oz
800g	1lb 12oz
850g	1lb 14oz
900g	2lb
950g	2lb 2oz
1kg	2lb 4oz

VOLUME

METRIC	IMPERIAL
30ml	1fl oz
50ml	2fl oz
75ml	2½fl oz
100ml	3½fl oz
125ml	4fl oz
150ml	¼ pint
175ml	6fl oz
200ml	7fl oz
225ml	8fl oz
250ml	9fl oz
300ml	½ pint
350ml	12fl oz
400ml	14fl oz
425ml	¾ pint
450ml	16fl oz
500ml	18fl oz
600ml	1 pint
700ml	1¼ pint
850ml	1½ pint
1 litre	1¾ pint

SPOON MEASURES

METRIC	IMPERIAL
5ml	1tsp
10ml	2tsp
15ml	1tbsp
30ml	2tbsp
45ml	3tbsp
60ml	4tbsp
75ml	5tbsp

TEMPERATURE

GAS MARK	ºF	ºC
¼	250	120
1	275	140
2	300	150
3	325	160
4	350	180
5	375	190
6	400	200
7	425	220
8	450	230
9	475	240

ºF		ºC
212	BOILING	100
122		50
113		45
104		40
95		35
86		30
77		25
68		20
59		15
50		10
41		5
32	FREEZING	0

NOTES

SPECIAL DATES

JANUARY

....

FEBRUARY

....

MARCH

....

APRIL

....

MAY

....

JUNE

SPECIAL DATES

JULY

....

AUGUST

....

SEPTEMBER

....

OCTOBER

....

NOVEMBER

....

DECEMBER

JANUARY

1
MON

New Year's Holiday (UK & Republic of Ireland)

2
TUE

Holiday (Scotland)

3
WED

4
THU

5
FRI

6
SAT

7
SUN

CAFFE LATTE GINGERBREAD CHEESECAKE

Inspired by the wonderful old-style Flemish coffee shops (now very much back in fashion), this cheesecake has a base made from those ultra-thin, very crisp, spicy biscuits traditionally served with coffee, and a rich, velvety, coffee-flavoured filling spiked with glacé ginger. It looks really impressive, but is not a difficult bake.

JANUARY

8
MON

....

9
TUE

....

10
WED

....

11
THU

....

12
FRI

....

13
SAT

....

14
SUN

CAFFE LATTE GINGERBREAD CHEESECAKE

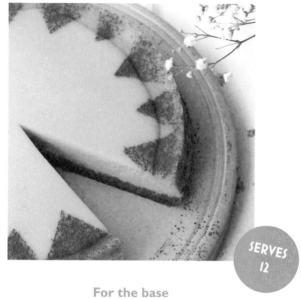

SERVES 12

For the base
190g Crisp Spiced Wafers, store-bought thin, crisp ginger or spice biscuits
70g unsalted butter, melted

For the filling
800g full-fat cream cheese
150ml soured cream
4 medium eggs, at room temperature
300g caster sugar
1 teaspoon vanilla extract
1 slightly rounded tablespoon instant coffee (granules or powder)
1 tablespoon boiling water
1 tablespoon coffee liqueur
40g ready-chopped glacé ginger

To finish
cocoa powder, for dusting

You will need
1 x 23cm springclip tin, greased with butter
and base-lined; a baking sheet

JANUARY

15
MON

16
TUE

17
WED

18
THU

19
FRI

20
SAT

21
SUN

CAFFE LATTE GINGERBREAD CHEESECAKE

1. To make the cheesecake base, heat the oven to 150°C/300°F/Gas 2. Crush the spiced wafers in a food processor, or by putting them into a plastic bag and bashing with a rolling pin. Tip the crumbs into a bowl and stir in the melted butter until thoroughly combined. Transfer the mixture to the prepared tin and press on to the base with the back of a spoon to make an even layer. Bake in the heated oven for 10 minutes. Leave to cool while you make the filling.

2. Put the cream cheese, soured cream, eggs, sugar and vanilla extract into a food processor and blitz until the mixture is very smooth and creamy. Transfer 200ml to a measuring jug and set aside for the topping. Dissolve the coffee in the boiling water, then stir in the coffee liqueur. Add to the mixture remaining in the processor along with the glacé ginger, then 'pulse' a few times until thoroughly combined.

3. Set the springclip tin on a baking sheet. Pour the coffee filling on top of the biscuit base. Place the tin, on the baking sheet, in the heated oven and bake for 1 hour – the cheesecake filling will still 'wobble' if you gently jiggle the tin but the top should be just set. Remove the cheesecake, on its baking sheet, from the oven. Starting in the centre, carefully pour the reserved creamy white filling mixture on top, if possible leaving a 1cm border of coffee-coloured filling showing all round the edge.

4. Return the cheesecake to the oven and bake for a further 20–30 minutes until the filling has just a slight wobble. Turn off the oven and leave the cheesecake inside, with the door slightly ajar, to cool for 1 hour. After this time, remove the cheesecake from the oven and run a round-bladed knife around inside the tin to loosen the cheesecake, then leave to cool completely. Once cold, cover with clingfilm and chill overnight.

5. Unclip the side of the tin and set the cheesecake on a serving platter. Dust with cocoa powder just before serving – for extra effect use a stencil. Keep any leftovers in the fridge.

JANUARY

22
MON

23
TUE

24
WED

25
THU

26
FRI

27
SAT

28
SUN

NOTES

JANUARY/FEBRUARY

29
MON

30
TUE

31
WED

1
THU

2
FRI

3
SAT

4
SUN

BIRD'S NEST

Sugarpaste flowers are easy to find in shops that sell cake and baking supplies, or online. Pretty sugar-coated eggs in assorted colours and sizes are easier to find around Easter time, which makes this a wonderful springtime birthday cake.

FEBRUARY

5
MON

....

6
TUE

....

7
WED

....

8
THU

....

9
FRI

....

10
SAT

....

11
SUN

BIRD'S NEST

SERVES
12

For the vanilla sponge
250g unsalted butter
250g caster sugar
2 teaspoons vanilla extract
4 eggs, lightly beaten
200g plain flour
50g cornflour
3 teaspoons baking powder
a pinch of salt
4 tablespoons milk
6 tablespoons seedless raspberry or
apricot jam

For the chocolate buttercream
250g unsalted butter
500g icing sugar, sifted
75g cocoa powder, sifted
2 tablespoons milk
1 tablespoon golden syrup
2 teaspoons vanilla extract

For the decoration
100g dark chocolate, chopped
75g milk chocolate, chopped
100g shredded wheat biscuit cereal,
lightly crushed
milk chocolate-coated stick biscuits
sugarpaste flowers in different sizes
assorted sugar-coated chocolate eggs

You will also need
2 x 20cm round cake tins
1 x 18cm round cake tin
12cm plain round cutter
disposable piping bag
bird decorations

FEBRUARY

12
MON

13
TUE

14
WED

Ash Wednesday / St. Valentine's Day

15
THU

16
FRI

Chinese New Year

17
SAT

18
SUN

BIRD'S NEST

Make the vanilla sponge

1. Preheat the oven to 180°C/160°C fan/ Gas 4 and position the shelves as close to the middle as possible, leaving enough space between them for the cakes to rise. Grease the cake tins and line the bases with discs of buttered baking parchment.

2. Cream the butter with the caster sugar and vanilla extract until thoroughly combined, pale and light. This will take at least 3 minutes using a stand mixer and longer if using a hand-held electric beater or a wooden spoon or spatula. Scrape down the sides of the bowl and then gradually add the beaten eggs, one at a time, mixing well between each addition.

3. Sift the flour, cornflour, baking powder and salt into the bowl, add the milk and beat until smooth, mixing slowly at first and gradually increasing the speed. Scrape down the bowl and mix again for about 30 seconds until the batter is silky smooth.

4. Divide the cake mix evenly between the prepared tins and level them with a palette knife or the back of a spoon. Bake for 20 minutes until golden, well risen and a skewer inserted into the centres comes out clean. Leave to rest in the tins for 3–4 minutes and then carefully tum out onto a wire rack and leave until cold.

Assemble the cake

5. Chop the butter into the bowl of a stand mixer or a large mixing bowl and beat until pale and light.

6. Remove the bowl from the power source, if using, and gradually add the sifted icing sugar and cocoa powder along with the vanilla extract and milk. Once all the icing sugar and cocoa powder have been incorporated, add the golden syrup and return the bowl to the mixer. Beat for a further minute or so, until the mixture is light and creamy.

7. Lay the sponge layers on the work surface and level the tops, if necessary. using a large serrated knife. Spread one of the big layers with half the jam. Spoon a third of the buttercream into a large disposable piping bag and snip the end to make a 1cm hole. Pipe the buttercream on top of the jam in an even layer and spread it smooth using a palette knife. Place the second big layer on top and spread it with the remaining jam and half the remaining buttercream.

8. Use the round cutter to cut out a circle from the middle of the smaller cake. Lay the sponge ring on top of the other cake layers and cover the whole cake in the rest of the buttercream, creating texture with the palette knife.

Decorate the nest

9. Melt all the chocolate and the butter in a heatproof bowl over a pan of barely simmering water, making sure the bottom of the bowl doesn't touch the water, or in the microwave on a low setting. Stir until smooth and leave to cool for 5 minutes.

10. Tip the crushed shredded wheat into the melted chocolate, stir to coat and press onto the sponge ring to form a bird's nest shape. Leave to set.

11. Break the chocolate-coated biscuit sticks into pieces and scatter them around the base of the cake to look like twigs. Press sugarpaste flowers around the sides, fill the nest with eggs and place a few feathered birds on top before serving.

FEBRUARY

19
MON

20
TUE

21
WED

22
THU

23
FRI

24
SAT

25
SUN

NOTES

FEBRUARY/MARCH

26
MON

27
TUE

28
WED

1
THU

St. David's Day (Wales)

2
FRI

3
SAT

4
SUN

FRESH HERB FOUGASSE

Packed with aromatic fresh herbs – rosemary, thyme and sage – and fruity olive oil, and finished with crushed sea salt, this golden, crisp bread is redolent of the sunny Mediterranean. Enjoy it warm.

MARCH

5
MON

....

6
TUE

....

7
WED

....

8
THU

....

9
FRI

....

10
SAT

....

11
SUN

Mothering Sunday (UK)

FRESH HERB FOUGASSE

MAKES 2

Ingredients
500g strong white bread flour, plus extra for dusting
10g fine sea salt
10g fast-action dried yeast (from 2 x 7g sachets)
2 tablespoons olive oil, plus extra for brushing/spraying
350ml warm water
2 teaspoons chopped fresh rosemary, plus extra to finish
2 teaspoons chopped fresh thyme
2 teaspoons chopped fresh sage
fine semolina, for dusting
½ teaspoon dried oregano crushed sea salt, to finish

You will also need
1 square plastic container, about 3 litre capacity, oiled
2 baking sheets, lined with baking paper
a water-spray bottle

MARCH

12
MON

....

13
TUE

....

14
WED

....

15
THU

....

16
FRI

....

17
SAT

St. Patrick's Day (Ireland)
....

18
SUN

FRESH HERB FOUGASSE

1. Put the flour, fine salt and yeast into the bowl of a free-standing electric mixer fitted with the dough hook – take great care not to put the salt directly on top of the yeast. Add the olive oil and three-quarters of the warm water, then start mixing on a low speed. As the dough begins to come together, add the remaining water very slowly, trickling it into the bowl, then mix/knead for a further 6–8 minutes on a medium speed to make a soft, smooth, pliable dough.

2. Add the rosemary, thyme and sage and mix for 1 minute until the herbs are evenly distributed in the dough. When the dough is thoroughly kneaded it will be very elastic – you should be able to stretch it away from the sides and base of the bowl. Transfer the dough to the oiled container, cover with a snap-on lid or clingfilm and leave to rise for about 1 hour until at least doubled in size, and bouncy and shiny.

3. Mix together equal quantities of white flour and semolina, and use to heavily dust the worktop. Carefully tip the dough on to this: it will be quite loose and flowing but don't worry! Divide in half. Lift each piece of dough on to a prepared baking sheet and gently spread out to a flat oval.

4. Using a pizza wheel-cutter, make 2 cuts down the middle of one oval, starting and stopping 2cm from each end, then make 6 diagonal cuts in the dough on both sides of this central cut, to form a leaf design. Stretch the dough out to emphasise the holes you've cut, to ensure they don't close up during rising. Repeat with the second dough oval.

5. Place each baking sheet in a large plastic bag, slightly inflate it to prevent the dough from sticking to the plastic as it rises and secure the ends. Leave to rise for 20 minutes. Towards the end of this time heat the oven to 220°C/425°F/Gas 7.

6. Uncover the loaves, then either spray them with a little olive oil using a water-spray bottle, or drizzle the oil over them. Sprinkle the dried oregano over the loaves. Bake for 15–20 minutes until the fougasses are nicely golden and sound hollow when tapped on the underside. Remove from the oven and, while still hot, brush with more olive oil, then sprinkle with crushed sea salt. Serve warm, as soon as possible.

MARCH

19
MON

St. Patrick's Day Holiday (Ireland)

20
TUE

21
WED

22
THU

23
FRI

24
SAT

25
SUN

Daylight Saving Begins

NOTES

MARCH/APRIL

26
MON

27
TUE

28
WED

29
THU

30
FRI

31
SAT

1
SUN

TRADITIONAL HOT CROSS BUNS

Rich with spices and studded with vine fruits and chopped mixed peel,
the buns are finished with a piped dough cross before baking and
glazed after baking for a brilliant shine.

APRIL

2
MON

Easter Monday (UK & Republic of Ireland)

3
TUE

4
WED

5
THU

6
FRI

7
SAT

8
SUN

TRADITIONAL HOT CROSS BUNS

MAKES 12 BUNS

Ingredients
350g strong white bread flour, plus extra for dusting
100g wholegrain bread flour (wheat or spelt)
7g salt
3 tablespoons caster sugar
2 teaspoons mixed spice
7g sachet fast-action dried yeast
50g unsalted butter, at room temperature, diced
125g dried mixed fruit and peel
2 medium eggs, at room temperature
175ml lukewarm milk

For the piped cross
4 tablespoons strong white bread flour
about 2 tablespoons cold water

For the glaze
4 tablespoons very hot milk
2 tablespoons caster sugar

APRIL

9
MON

10
TUE

11
WED

12
THU

13
FRI

14
SAT

15
SUN

TRADITIONAL HOT CROSS BUNS

1. Combine both the flours, salt, sugar and mixed spice in a large mixing bowl or the bowl of a free-standing mixer. Sprinkle the yeast into the bowl and mix in. When thoroughly combined, add the pieces of butter and rub into the flour mixture using just the tips of your fingers. When the mixture looks like fine crumbs mix in the dried fruit mixture. Make a well in the centre.

2. Add the eggs to the lukewarm milk and beat with a fork until thoroughly combined, then pour into the well in the flour mixture. Using your hand, or the dough hook attachment of the mixer on slow speed, gradually work the liquid into the flour to make a soft but not sticky dough. Flours vary so if there are dry crumbs in the base of the bowl, or if the dough feels stiff and dry, work in more milk, a tablespoon at a time. If the dough sticks to the sides of the bowl, work in more flour; a tablespoon at a time.

3. Lightly flour the worktop and your fingers then turn out the dough and knead it thoroughly for 10 minutes or until it feels very elastic and silky smooth – try to use as little extra flour as possible for kneading as it can make the dough too dry. (You can also knead the dough for about 5 minutes using the dough hook on slow speed).

4. Return the dough to the bowl, if necessary, then cover it tightly with clingfilm or a snap-on lid. Leave to rise on the worktop until doubled in size – about 1 hour. Line a baking sheet with baking paper.

5. Uncover the risen dough and punch down (knock back) to deflate it. Weigh the deflated dough and divide it into 12 equal portions. Using your hands, shape each portion of dough into a neat ball then arrange them 3cm apart on the lined baking sheet. Slip the baking sheet into a large plastic bag, trapping in some air so the plastic doesn't stick to the dough, and tie the ends. Leave to prove and rise on the worktop until doubled in size – about 45 minutes. Towards the end of the rising time preheat the oven to 200°C (180°C Fan)/400°F/Gas 6.

6. To make the piped cross, put the 4 tablespoons strong white bread flour into a small bowl and stir in about 2 tablespoons of cold water to make a smooth, thick mixture that can be piped (you may not need all the water). Spoon into a disposable piping bag and snip off the tip. Uncover the buns and pipe a cross over the top of each one.

7. Bake the buns for 15 minutes, or until they are a good golden brown. Set the baking sheet on a wire rack while you glaze the buns: mix the 4 tablespoons very hot (just below boiling point) milk with the 2 tablespoons caster sugar; just until the sugar has dissolved, then quickly brush the hot, sticky glaze over the hot buns. Transfer the buns to a wire rack and leave to cool.

APRIL

16
MON

....

17
TUE

....

18
WED

....

19
THU

....

20
FRI

....

21
SAT

....

22
SUN

NOTES

APRIL

23
MON

St. George's Day (England)

24
TUE

25
WED

26
THU

27
FRI

28
SAT

29
SUN

NOTES

APRIL/MAY

30
MON

....

1
TUE

....

2
WED

....

3
THU

....

4
FRI

....

5
SAT

....

6
SUN

ANGEL CAKE WITH SOFT FRUITS AND COCONUT CREAM

Angel cake is the lightest, airiest cake of all and one that takes a little practice to get just right, as it relies on careful folding of flour into a soft meringue. In this version, individual cakes are covered in a delicious coconut cream for a completely dairy-free treat.

MAY

7
MON

May Day Holiday (UK & Republic of Ireland)

8
TUE

9
WED

10
THU

11
FRI

12
SAT

13
SUN

ANGEL CAKE WITH SOFT FRUITS AND COCONUT CREAM

MAKES 8 CAKES

Ingredients
vegetable oil, for brushing
65g plain flour, plus extra for dusting
75g icing sugar
6 medium egg whites, at room temperature
½ teaspoon cream of tartar
pinch of salt
75g caster sugar
1 teaspoon vanilla bean paste or extract

For the topping
2 x 160g tins coconut cream, chilled for several hours or overnight
2 tablespoons icing sugar
few drops of lemon juice
about 200g mixture of soft fruits e.g. raspberries, red and blackcurrants
and small strawberries

Special equipment
8 x 150ml metal pudding moulds, large baking sheet

MAY

14
MON

15
TUE

16
WED

17
THU

18
FRI

19
SAT

20
SUN

ANGEL CAKE WITH SOFT FRUITS AND COCONUT CREAM

1. Position the oven shelf on the lowest rack and preheat the oven to 180°C (160°C fan)/350°F/Gas 4. Brush the metal pudding moulds with oil. Sprinkle a little flour into each and turn until the base and sides are evenly coated in flour. Tap out the excess. Sift together the flour and icing sugar and put to one side for now.

2. Put the egg whites into a large, spotlessly clean bowl with the cream of tartar and salt. Gently whisk using a hand-held electric whisk until frothy. (Alternatively use a free-standing electric mixer.) Increase the mixer speed and whisk until the mixture stands in soft, floppy peaks when the whisk is lifted from the bowl. At this point start to add the caster sugar, a tablespoonful at a time. Whisk well between each addition until the meringue is glossy and forms soft peaks. Add the vanilla with the last of the sugar.

3. Sift half the flour mixture into the bowl and fold in using a large metal spoon. Sift in the remaining flour mixture and fold in.

4. Divide the mixture among the moulds, spreading the mixture gently to keep in as much air as possible. Fill each tin so the top of the mixture is 1 cm below the rim. Place on a baking sheet and bake for 10–12 minutes until slightly risen and springy to the touch. The crust should be pale, almost white, with the merest hint of colour in some areas.

5. Line a wire rack with baking paper to stop the cakes sticking. Loosen the edges of the cakes with the tip of a sharp knife and invert onto the paper leaving the metal moulds in place. If you try to remove the moulds while the cakes are still hot they're likely to collapse and lose their light airy texture. Once the cakes have cooled completely tap them out of the moulds onto the paper. If they refuse to budge, loosen the edges again, this time pushing the knife further down into the tins as the cake will have shrunk back slightly.

6. For the topping, scrape enough of the thick coconut cream that's set at the top of both 160g tins coconut cream into a bowl. As soon as you can get to the liquid underneath pour away 1 tablespoon from each tin (you won't need all of the liquid in the recipe). Scrape the rest of the coconut cream and the remaining liquid into the bowl and add the 2 tablespoons icing sugar and few drops of lemon juice. Whisk using a hand-held electric whisk, or a metal balloon whisk until the mixture is smooth and just holds its shape.

7. Spoon the cream onto the tops of the cakes and spread around the sides using a small palette knife until they're fairly smoothly coated. Arrange the 200g soft fruits on top to decorate. If the strawberries are large you might want to cut them in half first. Keep in a cool place until ready to serve.

MAY

21
MON

22
TUE

23
WED

24
THU

25
FRI

26
SAT

27
SUN

NOTES

MAY/JUNE

28
MON

Spring Holiday (UK)
....

29
TUE

....

30
WED

....

31
THU

....

1
FRI

....

2
SAT

....

3
SUN

FLOWER GARDEN

Mary Mary quite contrary... how many biscuits does your garden grow? Let your
imagination run wild when decorating this cake and use a variety of flower cutters.

JUNE

4
MON

5
TUE

6
WED

7
THU

8
FRI

9
SAT

10
SUN

FLOWER GARDEN

SERVES 12

For the vanilla sponge
250g unsalted butter
250g caster sugar
2 teaspoons vanilla extract
4 eggs, lightly beaten
200g plain flour
50g cornflour
3 teaspoons baking powder
a pinch of salt
4 tablespoons milk
6 tablespoons jam

For the shortbread biscuits
225g unsalted butter
150g icing sugar
I egg, lightly beaten
grated zest of ½ unwaxed lemon
I teaspoon vanilla bean paste
350g plain flour, plus extra for dusting
½ teaspoon baking powder
a pinch of salt

For the vanilla buttercream
250g unsalted butter
500g icing sugar
2 tablespoons milk
green food-colouring paste

For the decoration
500g royal icing sugar
assorted food-colouring pastes
mimosa sugar balls

You will also need
3 x 20cm round cake tins
2 x baking sheets
assorted flower, snail and caterpillar cutters
baking sheet
paper food-grade lolly sticks or wooden skewers
disposable piping bags

JUNE

11
MON

....

12
TUE

....

13
WED

....

14
THU

....

15
FRI

....

16
SAT

....

17
SUN

Father's Day

FLOWER GARDEN

Make the vanilla sponge

1. Preheat the oven to 180°C(160°C Fan)/350°F/Gas 4 and position the shelves as close to the middle as possible, leaving enough space between them for the cakes to rise. Grease the cake tins and line the bases with discs of buttered baking parchment.

2. Cream the butter with the caster sugar and vanilla extract until thoroughly combined, pale and light. This will take at least 3 minutes using a stand mixer and longer if using a hand-held electric beater or a wooden spoon or spatula. Scrape down the sides of the bowl and then gradually add the beaten eggs, one at a time, mixing well between each addition.

3. Sift the flour, cornflour, baking powder and salt into the bowl, add the milk and beat until smooth, mixing slowly at first and gradually increasing the speed. Scrape down the bowl and mix again for about 30 seconds, until the batter is silky smooth.

4. Divide the cake mix evenly between the prepared tins and spread it level with a palette knife or the back of a spoon. Bake for 20 minutes until golden, well risen and a skewer inserted into the centre of the sponges comes out clean. Leave to rest in the tins for 3–4 minutes and then carefully turn out onto a wire rack and leave until cold.

Make the biscuits

5. Cream the butter and icing sugar until pale, light and fluffy. This will be easiest and quickest using a stand mixer fitted with a paddle attachment but can also be done by hand with a wooden spoon. Scrape down the sides of the bowl with a spatula and gradually add the beaten egg, mixing well until smooth. Add the lemon zest and vanilla bean paste and mix again.

6. Sift the plain flour, baking powder and a pinch of salt into the bowl and mix until smooth. Flatten the dough into a disc, wrap it in cling film and chill for a couple of hours, or until firm. Line a baking sheet with baking parchment

7. Divide the chilled dough into 2 and roll out half to 2mm thick on a lightly dusted work surface. Use a large knife to cut out several 1 x 9cm fence posts – they can be a little uneven for a vintage fence look. You will need about 31–32 posts. Arrange on the prepared baking sheet and chill for 15 minutes.

8. Roll out the remaining dough to 2mm thick and stamp out a caterpillar and snail, if you have cutters, and as many flower shapes as you can in assorted shapes and sizes. Lay on the baking sheets and press a lolly stick or skewer into each flower. Chill for a further 15 minutes before baking all the biscuits for about 12 minutes, until pale golden. Leave to cool on wire racks until completely cold.

Prepare the royal icing

9. Tip the royal icing sugar into a bowl – it's only necessary to sift if the sugar is lumpy – and add cold water, a tablespoon at a time, mixing well between each addition until the icing is smooth, lump-free, and the desired consistency. Use a cocktail stick or wooden skewer to add dots of colour at a time and mix well

JUNE

18
MON

19
TUE

20
WED

21
THU

Longest Day

22
FRI

23
SAT

24
SUN

FLOWER GARDEN

between each addition until you reach the desired shade. Colours often intensify over time so less is often more, especially if you are after bright colours.

Set aside half and divide the remainder into 4 or 5 bowls. Tint each bowl a different colour. Ice the picket fence posts with white icing and then ice and decorate the flowers.

Decorate the biscuits

10. To pipe an outline or details on biscuits the icing will need to be thick enough to hold a firm trail when the whisk is lifted from the bowl. You can always add more water if the icing is too thick, but it's impossible to take it away if you make the icing too runny and you will need to add more sugar instead.

Spoon 3 tablespoons of the icing into a disposable piping bag and push and squeeze the icing towards the end. Twist the opening of the bag to prevent any icing escaping and secure with an elastic band.

Use sharp scissors to snip a tiny hole roughly 1–2mm wide from the tip and pipe a fine continuous line around the edge of each biscuit. Leave to set for 15 minutes. Add a drop of water to the remaining icing so that it is about the thickness of double cream and runny enough to no longer hold a ribbon trail. Use a small palette knife or teaspoon to carefully spread or 'flood' the runny icing onto the biscuit, inside the piped outline, in a smooth layer. Leave to set for 30 minutes before piping any further details onto each biscuit with the reserved piping icing. Use drops of icing to attach mimosa sugar balls to the centres of some of the flowers.

Assemble the cake

11. Chop the butter into a bowl and beat well until pale, very soft and light – how long this takes will depend on the temperature of your butter and kitchen and how fast you beat.

12. If using a stand mixer, remove the bowl for the next stage. Gradually add the icing sugar, in 3 or 4 batches, along with the vanilla extract and milk and mix to combine using a rubber spatula. Once all the sugar has been added, return the bowl to the mixer and beat again on medium speed until light and creamy. Adding the sugar slowly by hand and away from the power source prevents the sugar dust flying all over the kitchen and making a terrific mess. Tint half of it green and set it aside.

13. Lay the sponge layers on the work surface and use a large serrated knife to level the tops. Place one layer on a serving plate and spread it with jam and white buttercream. Repeat with the remaining layers and then cover the whole cake with the green buttercream.

14. Press the picket fence posts all around the edge of the cake. Push the flower cookies into the top, positioning them at different heights, and add the snail and caterpillar around the edge before serving.

JUNE/JULY

25
MON

26
TUE

27
WED

28
THU

29
FRI

30
SAT

1
SUN

CHOCOLATE-HAZELNUT ROCHERS

This recipe will extend your baking skills beyond simple meringues: the classic combo of hazelnuts and chocolate is mixed into a glossy stiff meringue to make craggy streaked mounds called 'rochers' (the French word for rocks). Sandwiched with whipped cream, they make a rich yet light dessert.

JULY

2
MON

3
TUE

4
WED

5
THU

6
FRI

7
SAT

8
SUN

CHOCOLATE-HAZELNUT ROCHERS

MAKES
6 PAIRS

Ingredients
100g blanched hazelnuts
100g dark chocolate (about 70% cocoa solids)
3 medium egg whites, at room temperature
good pinch of cream of tartar
175g caster sugar

For the filling
200ml double cream, well chilled
1 teaspoon hazelnut liqueur
OR vanilla extract

You will need
2 baking sheets, lined with baking paper

JULY

9
MON

10
TUE

11
WED

12
THU

Holiday (Northern Ireland)

13
FRI

14
SAT

15
SUN

CHOCOLATE-HAZELNUT ROCHERS

1. Heat the oven to 180°C (160°C Fan)/350°F/Gas 4. Tip the hazelnuts into a small baking dish or tin and toast in the heated oven for 7–10 minutes until golden brown. Leave to cool. Turn down the oven to 120°C (100°C Fan)/250°F/Gas ½.

2. Gently melt the chocolate, then leave to cool until needed. Meanwhile, use a large sharp knife to chop each hazelnut roughly into 2 or 3 pieces.

3. Put the egg whites and cream of tartar into a large bowl, or the bowl of a free-standing electric mixer fitted with the whisk attachment. Whisk the whites with a hand-held electric whisk, or the whisk attachment, to the soft peak stage. Whisk in the sugar a heaped tablespoon at a time to make a very stiff, glossy meringue.

4. Scatter the chopped nuts over the meringue, then drizzle the chocolate over the top. Using a large metal spoon or plastic spatula, gently fold the nuts and chocolate into the meringue using just 2 or 3 strokes to give a distinct, streaked/marbled effect.

5. Using a soup spoon or kitchen spoon, scoop up a heaped spoonful of the meringue mixture, then use a second spoon to gently push the mixture off and on to the lined baking sheet to make a craggy, rough-looking mound. Repeat to make 12 mounds, spacing them well apart to allow for expansion.

6. Bake in the heated oven for 2 hours until firm. Turn off the oven and leave the meringues inside the cooling oven until they are completely cold before carefully peeling them off the lining paper (they can be stored in an air tight container for up to 3 days).

7. Shortly before you want to assemble the rochers, chill a bowl for whipping the cream. Pour the well-chilled cream and the hazelnut liqueur or vanilla into the chilled bowl and whip the cream until it is very thick and just past soft peak stage – it needs to hold a shape.

8. Using an offset palette knife, swirl whipped cream over the flat base of a meringue, then sandwich with another (flat base to flat base). Repeat until they are all sandwiched. Eat immediately or cover lightly and keep in the fridge until ready to serve (best eaten the same day).

JULY

16
MON

17
TUE

18
WED

19
THU

20
FRI

21
SAT

22
SUN

NOTES

JULY

23
MON

24
TUE

25
WED

26
THU

27
FRI

28
SAT

29
SUN

NOTES

JULY/AUGUST

30
MON

....

31
TUE

....

1
WED

....

2
THU

....

3
FRI

....

4
SAT

....

5
SUN

STEAMED CHOCOLATE SPONGE WITH CHOCOLATE CUSTARD

A burst of nostalgia with this school pudding classic, but home-made it is so much better! The simple sponge is rich with cocoa and moist from steaming, and served with custard flavoured with melted chocolate.

AUGUST

6
MON

Holiday (Scotland & Republic of Ireland)

7
TUE

8
WED

9
THU

10
FRI

11
SAT

12
SUN

STEAMED CHOCOLATE SPONGE WITH CHOCOLATE CUSTARD

SERVES 8–10

For the sponge
100g unsalted butter, softened
150g caster sugar
2 medium eggs, at room temperature
200g self-raising flour
pinch of salt
25g cocoa powder
100ml milk

For the custard
600ml whipping cream
6 medium egg yolks
20g sugar
100g 70–75 per cent dark chocolate (Grenadan would be ideal)

Special equipment
1-litre pudding basin

AUGUST

13
MON

14
TUE

15
WED

16
THU

17
FRI

18
SAT

19
SUN

STEAMED CHOCOLATE SPONGE WITH CHOCOLATE CUSTARD

1. Butter the pudding basin well and place a disc of baking paper inside to cover the base. Then butter the disc as well.

2. To make the sponge, cream the butter and sugar together until the mixture is light and fluffy. Then beat in the eggs, one at a time.

3. Mix the flour with the salt, and sift the cocoa powder over the flour before mixing them all together. Add the flour and cocoa to the butter, sugar and egg mixture and fold it through thoroughly: Lastly add the milk, and continue folding until you have a smooth batter.

4. Pour the sponge batter into the prepared pudding basin. Take a large circle of baking paper or foil, and fold a pleat in the centre to allow room for the sponge to rise. Place this on top of the pudding basin to cover it and secure the foil well with string.

5. Place the pudding basin in a large, deep pan on a trivet or upturned saucer. Pour boiling water to halfway up the side of the pudding basin, and remember to top it up during the cooking time to prevent it boiling dry. Cover with a tight-fitting lid: a good way of ensuring this is to cover the pan with foil and then add the lid. Simmer the sponge over a low heat for 2 hours. Then remove the basin from the pan to a wire rack to cool a little before turning out the sponge onto your serving plate.

6. While the sponge is steaming you can make the custard. Put the 600ml cream into a pan to warm through over a low heat. Whisk the 6 egg yolks and 20g sugar together in a heatproof bowl. Then pour the warm cream onto the eggs and sugar; whisking all the time. Next pour the custard mixture back into the pan and cook, stirring continuously over a low heat, until the custard has thickened to your desired consistency. This will take 10−15 minutes, depending on how high your heat.

7. Put the 100g chocolate into the bowl that held the eggs and sugar; and when your custard is thickened pour it over the chocolate. Stir the custard through until the chocolate has melted into it and you have a smooth chocolate custard.

8. Serve the chocolate sponge with the custard; both the sponge and custard are delicious hot or cold.

AUGUST

20
MON

21
TUE

22
WED

23
THU

24
FRI

25
SAT

26
SUN

NOTES

AUGUST/SEPTEMBER

27
MON

Late Summer Holiday (UK)

28
TUE

29
WED

30
THU

31
FRI

1
SAT

2
SUN

GREEK LEMON-YOGHURT LOAF CAKE

A slice of this quick and easily mixed loaf cake – you just need a bowl and wooden spoon – is perfect with a cup of tea. The sponge has a bright yellow crumb with a moist texture and tangy flavour thanks to the inclusion of thick creamy yoghurt and light olive oil plus lemon zest. While the cake is still hot, a lemon and yoghurt glaze is added to give a shiny finish with a slight crunch.

SEPTEMBER

3
MON

4
TUE

5
WED

6
THU

7
FRI

8
SAT

9
SUN

GREEK LEMON-YOGHURT LOAF CAKE

SERVES 8

Ingredients
150g plain flour
2 teaspoons baking powder
good pinch of salt
50g ground almonds
200g caster sugar
finely grated zest of 1 large unwaxed lemon
3 medium eggs, at room temperature
125ml Greek-style yoghurt
125ml mild light olive oil

For the lemon glaze
125g icing sugar, sifted
finely grated zest of 1 large unwaxed lemon
1–1½ tablespoons Greek-style yoghurt

You will need
1 x 450g loaf tin, about 19 x 12.5 x 7.5cm, greased with butter
and lined with a long strip of baking paper

SEPTEMBER

10
MON

Rosh Hashanah (Jewish New Year)

11
TUE

Al Hijra

12
WED

13
THU

14
FRI

15
SAT

16
SUN

GREEK LEMON-YOGHURT LOAF CAKE

1. Heat the oven to 180°C(160°C Fan)/350°F/Gas 4. Sift the flour, baking powder, salt and ground almonds into a mixing bowl (tip in any almonds remaining in the sieve). Stir in the sugar and lemon zest, then make a well in the mixture.

2. Combine the eggs, yoghurt and oil in a measuring jug and beat well with a fork until well mixed. Pour into the well in the bowl, then beat everything together with a wooden spoon until thoroughly combined.

3. Scrape the mixture into the prepared tin, spreading evenly and making sure the corners are well filled. Bake in the heated oven for 55–65 minutes until well risen and a deep golden brown; a skewer inserted into the centre of the cake should come out clean.

4. Towards the end of the baking time make the lemon glaze so it will be ready when you need it. Sift the icing sugar into a bowl. Mix in the lemon zest, then stir in enough yoghurt to make a smooth, shiny glaze with the consistency of double cream.

5. As soon as the cake is ready, remove from the oven and set the tin on a wire rack. Leave the cake to firm up for 5 minutes. Run a round-bladed knife around the inside of the tin to loosen the loaf, then carefully lift it out, using the ends of the lining paper strip, and set the cake on the wire rack. Place a plate underneath the rack to catch drips. Spoon the glaze over the hot cake, letting the glaze slowly drip down the sides. Leave until the cake is cold and the glaze has set.

6. Serve cut in thick slices. Store, wrapped in foil or baking paper, in an airtight container and eat within 4 days – the flavours and aromas will be even more pronounced a day or so after baking.

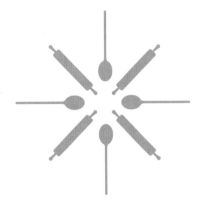

SEPTEMBER

17
MON

18
TUE

19
WED

Yom Kippur (Day of Atonement)

20
THU

21
FRI

The United Nations International Day of Peace

22
SAT

23
SUN

NOTES

SEPTEMBER

24
MON

....

25
TUE

....

26
WED

....

27
THU

....

28
FRI

....

29
SAT

....

30
SUN

NOTES

OCTOBER

1
MON

....

2
TUE

....

3
WED

....

4
THU

....

5
FRI

....

6
SAT

....

7
SUN

CHOCOLATE MAPLE TARTS WITH HAZELNUT BRITTLE

Combine a hazelnut pâte sucrée with maple jelly and a creamy white and milk chocolate filling for the ultimate chocolate dessert, adorned with an impressive nut brittle decoration.

OCTOBER

8
MON

....

9
TUE

....

10
WED

....

11
THU

....

12
FRI

....

13
SAT

....

14
SUN

CHOCOLATE MAPLE TARTS WITH HAZELNUT BRITTLE

MAKES 6

For the hazelnut pâte sucrée
25g hazelnuts
75g unsalted butter, at room temperature
2 tablespoons golden caster sugar
1 medium egg yolk
125g plain flour

For the filling
3 sheets leaf gelatine
150ml maple syrup
150g good quality white chocolate, chopped
150ml double cream
150g good quality milk chocolate, chopped

For the hazelnut brittle
25g unblanched hazelnuts, toasted and chopped
100g caster sugar

Special equipment
6 individual 10cm round loose-bottomed plain or fluted tart tins,
2cm deep and a baking sheet

OCTOBER

15
MON

16
TUE

17
WED

18
THU

19
FRI

20
SAT

21
SUN

CHOCOLATE MAPLE TARTS WITH HAZELNUT BRITTLE

1. First make the pastry. Heat a small, dry frying pan, add the nuts and heat for 4–5 minutes until the nuts are lightly toasted. Shake the pan frequently so they brown evenly. Leave to cool then blend in a food-processor until finely ground.

2. Put the butter and sugar in a bowl and cream together by beating with a wooden spoon until light and creamy. Beat in the egg yolk. Stir in the flour, about a third at a time. Add the cocoa powder and ground hazelnuts, then work the mixture together with your fingertips, along with 2 teaspoons of cold water (add a drop more if needed to bring the dough together), until it starts to clump together in big lumps and form a dough. Tip the dough onto the work surface and knead very briefly until smooth. Wrap in clingfilm and chill for 15 minutes in the freezer or 30 minutes in the fridge.

3. Roll out the pastry on a lightly floured surface to a 2mm thickness. Cut out six 13cm circles using a cutter or upturned bowl as a guide. Gather up the trimmings and re-roll them so you have enough pastry circles. Use to line the tins, easing the pastry into the corners and up the sides. Trim off the excess pastry around the tops. Prick the bases lightly with a fork and chill in the fridge for 15 minutes.

4. Preheat the oven to 200°C (180°C Fan)/400° F/Gas 6 and put a baking sheet in the oven to heat up. Line the pastry cases with circles of baking paper and fill with baking beans or uncooked rice. Place the tins on the hot baking sheet and blind bake for 15 minutes. Remove the paper and beans and bake for a further 5 minutes, or until the pastry looks cooked. Leave to cool in the cases.

5. Next make the maple jelly for the filling. Put the 3 leaf gelatine sheets in a bowl of cold water and leave to soften for 5 minutes. Put 75ml of the maple syrup in a small pan and bring just to the boil. Lift the leaf gelatine sheets from the water. These will be floppy but still hold together. Let the excess water drip off and then, off the heat, lower the gelatine into the syrup. Shake the pan and you'll see the gelatine dissolve. Once completely dissolved, pour into a jug and add the remaining 75ml maple syrup. Chill in the fridge until thickened but not set.

6. Spoon the jelly into the tart cases and spread to the edges with the back of a teaspoon. Chill for at least 30 minutes until completely set.

7. To make the chocolate layers, put the 150g white chocolate and 75ml of the double cream in a small heatproof bowl and set over a pan of barely simmering water, making sure the bottom of the bowl doesn't touch the water. Heat for 1–2 minutes until the chocolate shows signs of melting. At this point turn off the heat but leave the bowl over the pan until the chocolate has melted, stirring the mixture occasionally.

8. Once the chocolate has melted, remove the bowl from the pan and leave to cool. At the point where it's thickened,

OCTOBER

22
MON

....

23
TUE

....

24
WED

....

25
THU

....

26
FRI

....

27
SAT

....

28
SUN

Daylight Saving Ends

CHOCOLATE MAPLE TARTS WITH HAZELNUT BRITTLE

but not setting, spoon it over the jelly and spread to the edges. Chill in the fridge while you prepare the 150g milk chocolate layer in the same way, using the remaining 75ml cream. Once cool, spoon into the tarts and spread level. Return to the fridge.

9. To make the hazelnut brittle, lightly oil a baking sheet. Scatter the 25g chopped hazelnuts onto the baking sheet in an even layer. Put the 100g caster sugar and 2 tablespoons water in a small pan and heat gently without stirring until the sugar dissolves and the sugar syrup is clear. This will take about 8–10 minutes. Once the syrup is completely clear bring it to the boil and boil for about 5 minutes until the syrup turns to a golden amber colour. Immediately remove from the heat and drizzle the syrup in a fine stream over the nuts on the baking sheet. Leave for at least 30 minutes until completely brittle.

10. Break the brittle into shards and use to decorate the centres of the tarts. Transfer to serving plates.

Try something different
For a slightly less sweet version, use dark chocolate instead of the white chocolate. Omit the nut brittle and arrange a circle of roughly chopped toasted hazelnuts around the edges. Dust these lightly with cocoa powder.

OCTOBER/NOVEMBER

29
MON

Holiday (Republic of Ireland)

30
TUE

31
WED

Halloween

1
THU

2
FRI

3
SAT

4
SUN

BLACKBERRY AND APPLE BUCKLE

An old-fashioned buckle, where fruit is combined with a very light, egg-rich, buttery sponge and topped with a crunchy crumble, is a good, simple way to use up a windfall of delicious summer and autumn fruit. You can adapt this recipe to whatever fruit is available – here it's tangy cooking blackberries and tart eating apples, but do try blueberries, pears, large firm raspberries, and firm nectarines or peaches. The name of the dish comes from the way the topping buckles or dimples over the very soft, just-set filling.

NOVEMBER

5
MON

Guy Fawkes Night

6
TUE

7
WED

Diwali

8
THU

9
FRI

10
SAT

11
SUN

Remembrance Sunday

BLACKBERRY AND APPLE BUCKLE

SERVES 6

For the topping
90g plain flour
finely grated zest of ½ medium
unwaxed lemon
70g light muscovado sugar
70g unsalted butter, chilled and diced

For the base
150g tangy blackberries
1 medium Braeburn or other tart eating apple
115g unsalted butter, softened
100g caster sugar
finely grated zest of ½ medium
unwaxed lemon
2 medium eggs, at room temperature, beaten to mix
75g plain flour
1 teaspoon baking powder

To serve
icing sugar, for dusting yoghurt or cream

You will need
1 baking dish/pie dish, about 1.5 litre capacity, greased with butter

NOVEMBER

12
MON

13
TUE

14
WED

15
THU

16
FRI

17
SAT

18
SUN

BLACKBERRY AND APPLE BUCKLE

1. Heat the oven to 180°C (160°C Fan)/350°F/Gas 4. Make the topping first so it can firm up in the fridge while you make the filling. Mix the flour, lemon zest and sugar (press out any lumps) in a mixing bowl. Add the pieces of butter and rub in until the mixture looks like very coarse crumbs. Cover the bowl and keep in the fridge until needed.

2. Rinse the berries, then tip on to a plate lined with kitchen paper and leave to dry. Peel, quarter and core the apple, then chop into chunks about 1 cm. Transfer to a bowl and gently mix in the blackberries.

3. Put the softened butter into a mixing bowl, or the bowl of a free-standing electric mixer fitted with the whisk attachment. Beat with a wooden spoon or hand-held electric whisk, or the whisk attachment, until creamy and mayonnaise-like. Add the sugar and lemon zest and beat thoroughly until the mixture is very light and fluffy. Gradually add the eggs, a tablespoon at a time, beating well after each addition.

4. Scrape down the sides of the bowl. Sift the flour and baking powder into the bowl and fold in with a plastic spatula or large metal spoon until just combined. Add the blackberries and chopped apple to the bowl and gently fold in until evenly distributed.

5. Spoon the mixture into the buttered dish and spread evenly. Scatter the topping mixture over the filling in an even layer. Bake in the heated oven for 35–40 minutes until golden brown and crisp. Remove from the oven, dust with icing sugar and eat warm with yoghurt or cream.

NOVEMBER

19
MON

20
TUE

21
WED

22
THU

23
FRI

24
SAT

25
SUN

NOTES

NOVEMBER/DECEMBER

26
MON

27
TUE

28
WED

29
THU

30
FRI

St. Andrew's Day (Scotland)

1
SAT

2
SUN

JEWELLED CROWN

Decorate the shortbread crown biscuits as elaborately as you like, or dare, for this cake and assemble it shortly before serving.

DECEMBER

3
MON

....

4
TUE

....

5
WED

....

6
THU

....

7
FRI

....

8
SAT

....

9
SUN

JEWELLED CROWN

SERVES 12

For the vanilla sponge
250g unsalted butter
250g caster sugar
4 eggs, lightly beaten
2 teaspoons vanilla extract
200g plain flour
50g cornflour
3 teaspoons baking powder
a pinch of salt
4 tablespoons milk
2–3 tablespoons raspberry jam

For the shortbread biscuits
225g unsalted butter
150g icing sugar
1 egg, lightly beaten
grated zest of ½ unwaxed lemon
1 teaspoon vanilla bean paste
350g plain flour, plus extra for dusting
½ teaspoon baking powder
a pinch of salt

For the vanilla buttercream
250g unsalted butter
500g icing sugar
2 teaspoons vanilla extract
3 tablespoons milk

For the decoration
clear fruit-flavoured boiled sweets
200g royal icing sugar
jelly diamonds
silver and gold sugar balls
sugar pearls
red sanding sugar

You will also need
3 x 18cm round cake tins
2 x baking sheets
Crown template
disposable piping bag
fake fur rope or ribbon

DECEMBER

10
MON

11
TUE

12
WED

13
THU

14
FRI

15
SAT

16
SUN

JEWELLED CROWN

Make the vanilla sponge

1. Preheat the oven to 180°C(160°C Fan)/350°F/Gas 4 and position the shelves as close to the middle as possible, leaving enough space between them for the cakes to rise. Grease the cake tins and line the bases with discs of buttered baking parchment.

2. Cream the butter with the caster sugar and vanilla extract until thoroughly combined, pale and light. This will take at least 3 minutes using a stand mixer and longer if using a hand-held electric beater or a wooden spoon or spatula. Scrape down the sides of the bowl and then gradually add the beaten eggs, one at a time, mixing well between each addition.

3. Sift the flour, cornflour, baking powder and salt into the bowl, add the milk and beat until smooth, mixing slowly at first and gradually increasing the speed. Scrape down the bowl and mix again for about 30 seconds until the batter is silky smooth.

4. Divide the cake mix evenly between the prepared tins, spreading it level with a palette knife or the back of a spoon. Bake for 20 minutes until golden, well risen and a skewer inserted into the centre of the cakes comes out clean. Leave to rest in the tins for 3–4 minutes and then carefully turn out onto a wire rack and leave until cold.

Make the biscuits

5. Cream the butter and icing sugar until pale, light and fluffy. This will be easiest and quickest using a stand mixer fitted with a paddle attachment but can also be done by hand with a wooden spoon. Scrape down the sides of the bowl with a spatula and gradually add the beaten egg, mixing well until smooth. Add the lemon zest and vanilla bean paste and mix again.

6. Sift the plain flour, baking powder and a pinch of salt into the bowl and mix until smooth. Flatten the dough into a disc, wrap it in cling film; chill for 2 hours. Line the baking sheets with baking parchment.

7. Roll out the chilled dough on a lightly floured work surface to about 2mm thick. Use the template in this diary to cut out 9–10 crown shapes (you will only need 8 for the cake, but make extras in case of accidents). Arrange on the prepared baking sheets and chill for 15 minutes.

8. Bake the chilled biscuits for 10 minutes, until firm and only just starting to colour, then remove from the oven and place 1 boiled sweet in the hole at the top of each biscuit and continue to cook for a further 2 minutes, until the shortbread is golden and the boiled sweet jewel has melted and filled the hole. Remove from the oven and leave to cool on the baking sheet.

Make the icing

9. Using the ingredients listed in the recipe to guide you, tip the royal icing sugar into a bowl – it's only necessary to sift if the sugar is lumpy – and add cold water, a tablespoon at a time, mixing well between each addition until the icing is smooth, lump-free, and the desired consistency. Use a cocktail stick or wooden skewer to add dots of colour at a time and mix well between each

DECEMBER

17
MON

18
TUE

19
WED

20
THU

21
FRI

Shortest Day

22
SAT

23
SUN

JEWELLED CROWN

addition until you reach the desired shade. Colours often intensify over time so less is often more, especially if you are after bright colours. Use dots of icing to stick jelly diamonds, sugar balls and pearls to the biscuits and then set aside for about 2 hours to set firm.

Assemble the cake

10. Chop the butter into a bowl and beat well until pale, very soft and light – how long this takes will depend on the temperature of your butter and kitchen and how fast you beat.

11. If using a stand mixer, remove the bowl for the next stage. Gradually add the icing sugar, in 3 or 4 batches, along with the vanilla extract and milk and mix to combine using a rubber spatula. Once all the sugar has been added, return the bowl to the mixer and beat again on medium speed until light and creamy. Adding the sugar slowly by hand and away from the power source prevents the sugar dust flying all over the kitchen and making a terrific mess.

12. Place the cake layers on the work surface and use a large serrated knife to level the tops. Place one layer on the serving plate and spread it with a tablespoon of jam. Spread the underside of the second layer with buttercream and sandwich the two together. Repeat with the third layer. Use a palette knife to cover the whole cake with buttercream, swirling the cream towards the centre on the top to resemble velvet folds, and sprinkle the top liberally with sanding sugar.

13. Just before serving, position the crown biscuits around the sides of the cake, securing with a little jam or buttercream and tie a piece of fake fur or a ribbon around the base.

DECEMBER

24
MON

....

25
TUE

Christmas Day
....

26
WED

Boxing Day / St. Stephen's Day (Republic of Ireland)
....

27
THU

....

28
FRI

....

29
SAT

....

30
SUN

JEWELLED CROWN
TEMPLATE

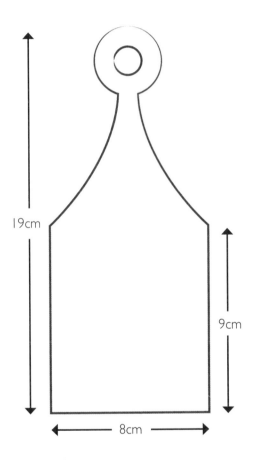

19cm

9cm

8cm

DEC 2018/JAN 2019

31
MON

New Year's Eve

....

1
TUE

....

2
WED

....

3
THU

....

4
FRI

....

5
SAT

....

6
SUN

NOTES

2019

JANUARY

M	T	W	T	F	S	S
	1	2	3	4	5	6
7	8	9	10	11	12	13
14	15	16	17	18	19	20
21	22	23	24	25	26	27
28	29	30	31			

FEBRUARY

M	T	W	T	F	S	S
				1	2	3
4	5	6	7	8	9	10
11	12	13	14	15	16	17
18	19	20	21	22	23	24
25	26	27	28			

MARCH

M	T	W	T	F	S	S
				1	2	3
4	5	6	7	8	9	10
11	12	13	14	15	16	17
18	19	20	21	22	23	24
25	26	27	28	29	30	31

APRIL

M	T	W	T	F	S	S
1	2	3	4	5	6	7
8	9	10	11	12	13	14
15	16	17	18	19	20	21
22	23	24	25	26	27	28
29	30					

MAY

M	T	W	T	F	S	S
	1	2	3	4	5	
6	7	8	9	10	11	12
13	14	15	16	17	18	19
20	21	22	23	24	25	26
27	28	29	30	31		

JUNE

M	T	W	T	F	S	S
					1	2
3	4	5	6	7	8	9
10	11	12	13	14	15	16
17	18	19	20	21	22	23
24	25	26	27	28	29	30

JULY

M	T	W	T	F	S	S
1	2	3	4	5	6	7
8	9	10	11	12	13	14
15	16	17	18	19	20	21
22	23	24	25	26	27	28
29	30	31				

AUGUST

M	T	W	T	F	S	S
			1	2	3	4
5	6	7	8	9	10	11
12	13	14	15	16	17	18
19	20	21	22	23	24	25
26	27	28	29	30	31	

SEPTEMBER

M	T	W	T	F	S	S
						1
2	3	4	5	6	7	8
9	10	11	12	13	14	15
16	17	18	19	20	21	22
23	24	25	26	27	28	29
30						

OCTOBER

M	T	W	T	F	S	S
	1	2	3	4	5	6
7	8	9	10	11	12	13
14	15	16	17	18	19	20
21	22	23	24	25	26	27
28	29	30	31			

NOVEMBER

M	T	W	T	F	S	S
				1	2	3
4	5	6	7	8	9	10
11	12	13	14	15	16	17
18	19	20	21	22	23	24
25	26	27	28	29	30	

DECEMBER

M	T	W	T	F	S	S
						1
2	3	4	5	6	7	8
9	10	11	12	13	14	15
16	17	18	19	20	21	22
23	24	25	26	27	28	29
30	31					

NOTES

ADDRESSES

NAME
....

ADDRESS
....

....

TEL
....

MOB
....

EMAIL
....

NAME
....

ADDRESS
....

....

TEL
....

MOB
....

EMAIL
....

NAME
....

ADDRESS
....

....

TEL
....

MOB
....

EMAIL

NOTES

ADDRESSES

NAME
....

ADDRESS
....

....

TEL
....

MOB
....

EMAIL
....

NAME
....

ADDRESS
....

....

TEL
....

MOB
....

EMAIL
....

NAME
....

ADDRESS
....

....

TEL
....

MOB
....

EMAIL

NOTES

ADDRESSES

NAME

....

ADDRESS

....

....

TEL

....

MOB

....

EMAIL

....

NAME

....

ADDRESS

....

....

TEL

....

MOB

....

EMAIL

....

NAME

....

ADDRESS

....

....

TEL

....

MOB

....

EMAIL

NOTES

NOTES

NOTES